FABER MUSIC PRESENTS

THE ESSENTIAL SHOWTUNES COLLECTION

25 GREAT SHOWTUNES ARRANGED FOR INTERMEDIATE PIANO SOLO

ARRANGED BY RICHARD HARRIS

FABER *ff* MUSIC

© 2008 by Faber Music Ltd
This edition first published in 2008
3 Queen Square London WC1N 3AU
Music processed by Jeanne Roberts
Cover design by Kenosha
Printed in England by Caligraving Ltd
All rights reserved

ISBN10: 0-571-52782-5
EAN13: 978-0-571-52782-3

To buy Faber Music publications or to find out about the full range of titles available
please contact your local music retailer or Faber Music sales enquiries:

Faber Music Ltd, Burnt Mill, Elizabeth Way, Harlow CM20 2HX
Tel: +44 (0) 1279 82 89 82   Fax: +44 (0) 1279 82 89 83
sales@fabermusic.com   fabermusic.com

CONTENTS

THERE'S NO BUSINESS LIKE SHOW BUSINESS (FROM *ANNIE GET YOUR GUN*) *page* 4

ANY DREAM WILL DO (FROM *JOSEPH AND HIS AMAZING TECHNICOLOR® DREAMCOAT*) *page* 6

IF I WERE A RICH MAN (FROM *FIDDLER ON THE ROOF*) *page* 8

WAND'RIN' STAR (FROM *PAINT YOUR WAGON*) *page* 10

CABARET (FROM *CABARET*) *page* 12

WE WILL ROCK YOU (FROM *WE WILL ROCK YOU*) *page* 14

CHEEK TO CHEEK (FROM *TOP HAT*) *page* 17

AQUARIUS (FROM *HAIR*) *page* 20

WELL, DID YOU EVAH? (FROM *HIGH SOCIETY*) *page* 22

THAT'S ENTERTAINMENT (FROM *THE BAND WAGON*) *page* 24

SINGIN' IN THE RAIN (FROM *SINGIN' IN THE RAIN*) *page* 26

I COULD HAVE DANCED ALL NIGHT (FROM *MY FAIR LADY*) *page* 28

DON'T RAIN ON MY PARADE (FROM *FUNNY GIRL*) *page* 30

I GOT RHYTHM (FROM *GIRL CRAZY*) *page* 32

AND ALL THAT JAZZ (FROM *CHICAGO*) *page* 34

CONSIDER YOURSELF (FROM *OLIVER!*) *page* 36

LUCK BE A LADY (FROM *GUYS AND DOLLS*) *page* 38

ANYTHING GOES (FROM *ANYTHING GOES*) *page* 40

FLASHDANCE (WHAT A FEELING) (FROM *FLASHDANCE*) *page* 42

FAME (FROM *FAME*) *page* 44

SEND IN THE CLOWNS (FROM *A LITTLE NIGHT MUSIC*) *page* 46

SUMMER NIGHTS (FROM *GREASE*) *page* 48

MAMMA MIA (FROM *MAMMA MIA!*) *page* 51

MEMORY (FROM *CATS*) *page* 54

(I'VE HAD) THE TIME OF MY LIFE (FROM *DIRTY DANCING*) *page* 57

THERE'S NO BUSINESS LIKE SHOW BUSINESS
(FROM *ANNIE GET YOUR GUN*)

Words and Music by Irving Berlin

Bright and up tempo ♩ = c.160

There's no bus-'ness like show bus-'ness like no bus-'ness I know. Ev-'ry-thing a-bout it is ap-peal-ing, ev-'ry-thing the traf-fic will al-low. No-where could you get that hap-py feel-ing when you are steal-ing that ex-tra bow. There's

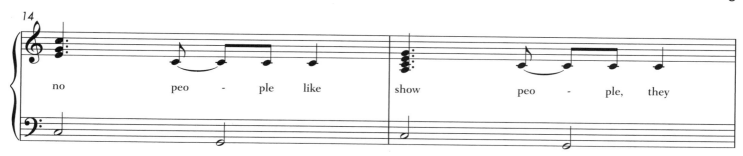

no peo - ple like show peo - ple, they

smile when __ they are low. E - ven with a tur - key that you

know will fold; _____ you may be strand - ed out

in the cold. __ Still you would - n't change it for a

sack of gold. __ Let's go on __ with the show!

ANY DREAM WILL DO
(FROM *JOSEPH AND HIS AMAZING TECHNICOLOR® DREAMCOAT*)

Music by Andrew Lloyd Webber Lyrics by Tim Rice

IF I WERE A RICH MAN
(FROM *FIDDLER ON THE ROOF*)

Words by Sheldon Harnick
Music by Jerry Bock

Carlin Music Corp

real wood-en floors be - low._____ There could be no - where just for

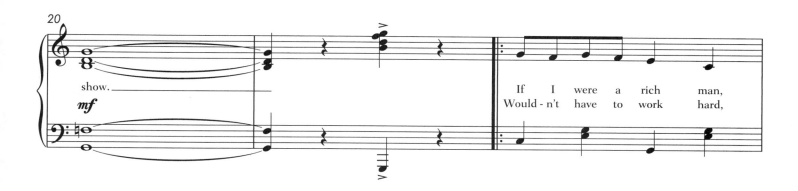

show._____

If I were a rich man,
Would-n't have to work hard,

Dai - die, dee - die, dai - die, dig - guh, dig - guh, dee - die, dai - die, dum.
Dai - die, dee - die, dai - die, dig - guh, dig - guh, dee - die, dai - die, dum.

All day long I'd bid - dy, bid - dy bum, If I were a wealth - y
If I were a bid - dy, bid - dy rich,

man. dig - guh, dig - guh, dee - die, dai - die man.

WAND'RIN' STAR
(FROM *PAINT YOUR WAGON*)

Words by Alan Jay Lerner
Music by Frederick Loewe

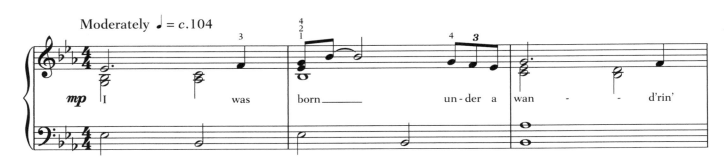

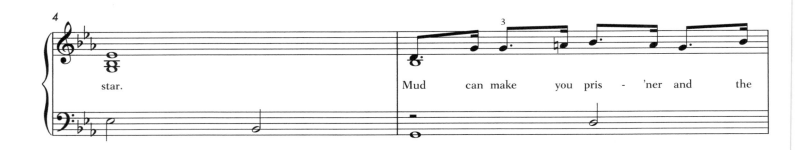

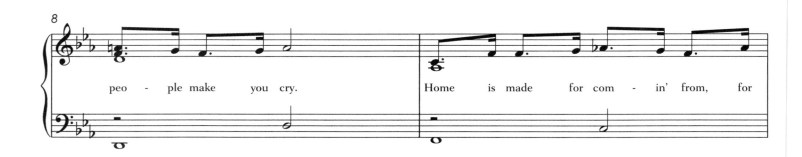

CABARET
(FROM CABARET)

Words by Fred Ebb
Music by John Kander

Lively ♩ = c.112

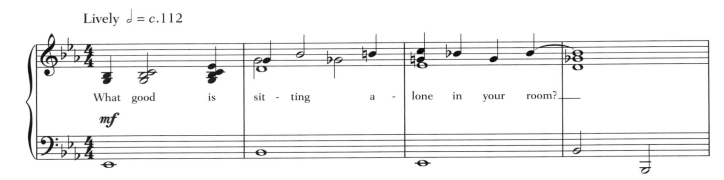

What good is sit - ting a - lone in your room?

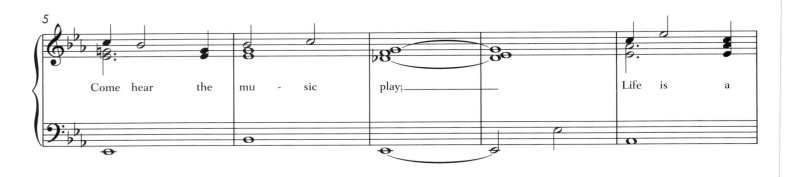

Come hear the mu - sic play; Life is a

Ca - ba - ret, old chum, Come to the Ca - ba -

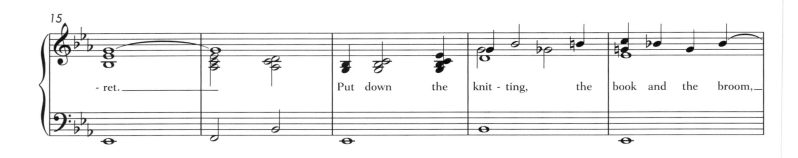

- ret. Put down the knit - ting, the book and the broom,

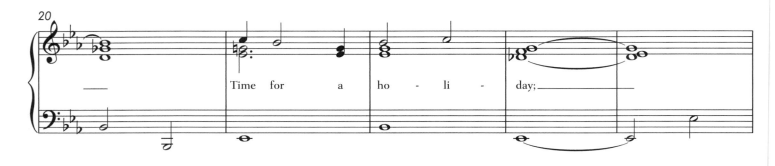

Time for a ho - li - day;

WE WILL ROCK YOU
(FROM *WE WILL ROCK YOU*)

Words and Music by Brian May

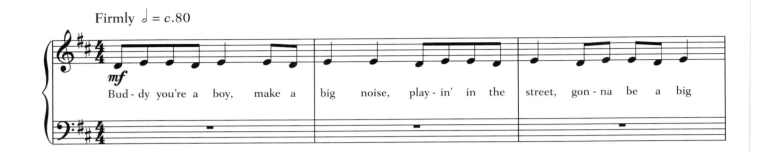

Firmly ♩ = c.80

mf

Bud - dy you're a boy, make a | big noise, play - in' in the | street, gon - na be a big

man some day, you got | mud on your face, you | big dis - grace, | kick - in' your can all

o - ver the place, sing - in' | We will, we will | rock you.

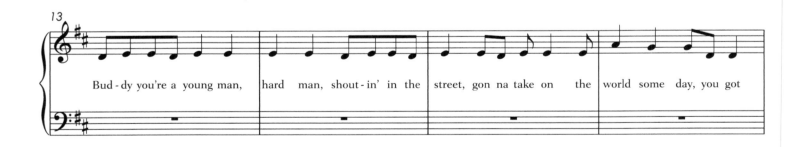

Bud - dy you're a young man, | hard man, shout - in' in the | street, gon na take on the | world some day, you got

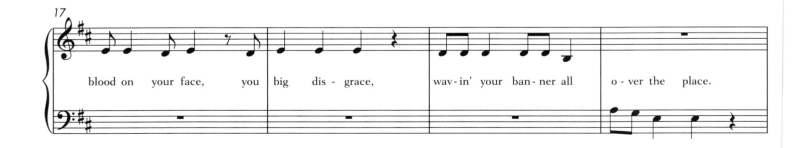

blood on your face, you | big dis - grace, | wav - in' your ban - ner all | o - ver the place.

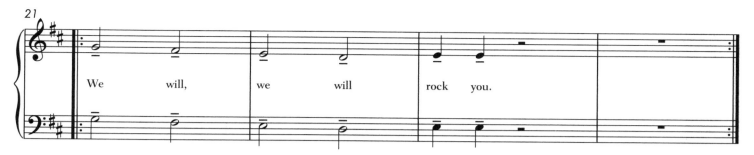

We will, we will rock you.

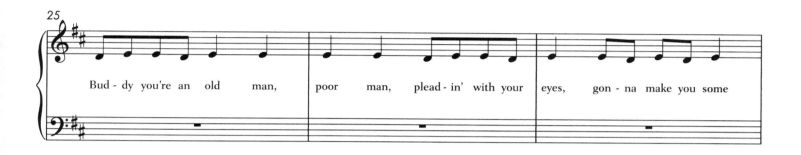

Bud - dy you're an old man, poor man, plead - in' with your eyes, gon - na make you some

peace some day, you got mud on your face, big dis - grace, some bo - dy bet - ter put you back

in - to your place. We will, we will rock you.

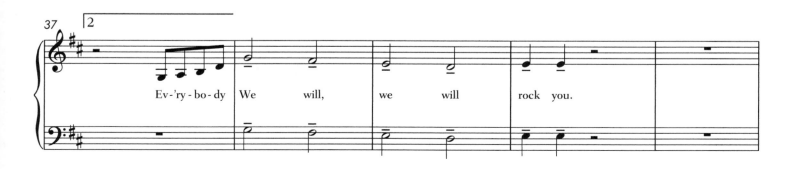

Ev - 'ry - bo - dy We will, we will rock you.

We will, we will rock you.

CHEEK TO CHEEK
(FROM *TOP HAT*)

Words and Music by Irving Berlin

AQUARIUS
(FROM *HAIR*)

Words by James Rado and Gerome Ragni
Music by Galt MacDermot

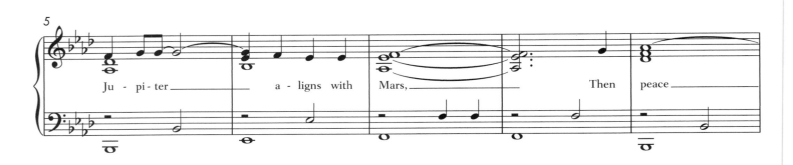

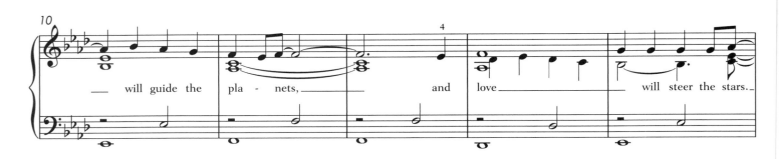

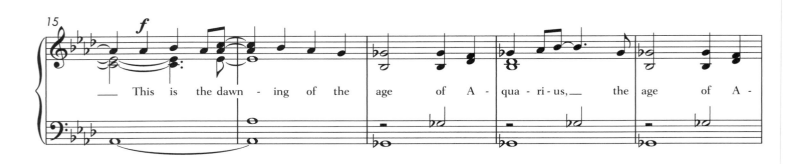

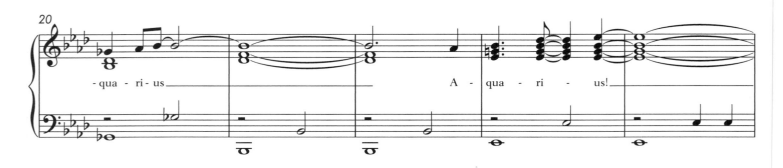

WELL, DID YOU EVAH?
(FROM *HIGH SOCIETY*)

Words and Music by Cole Porter

THAT'S ENTERTAINMENT
(FROM *THE BAND WAGON*)

Words by Howard Dietz
Music by Arthur Schwartz

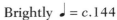

gay di - vor - cee who is af - ter her 'ex'.___ It can be

Oe - di - pus Rex,___ where a chap kills his fa - ther, and caus - es a lot of bo - ther. The

clerk___ who is thrown out of work___ by the boss___ who is

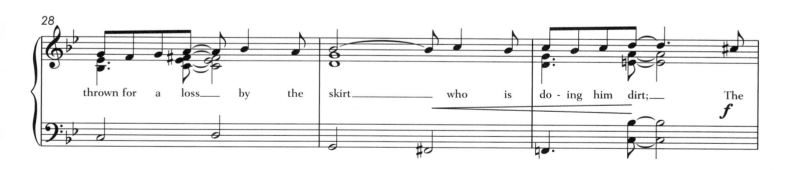

thrown for a loss___ by the skirt___ who is do - ing him dirt;___ The

world is a stage, the stage is a world of en - ter - tain - - ment!

SINGIN' IN THE RAIN
(FROM *SINGIN' IN THE RAIN*)

Words by Arthur Freed
Music by Nacio Herb Brown

I COULD HAVE DANCED ALL NIGHT
(FROM *MY FAIR LADY*)

Words by Alan Jay Lerner
Music by Frederick Loewe

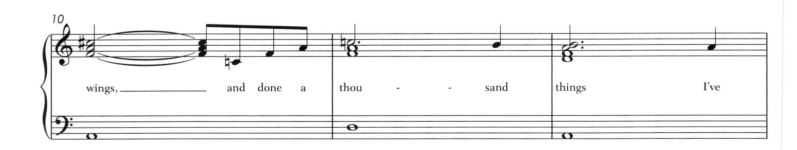

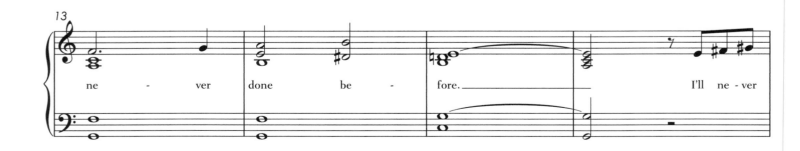

know _____ what made it so ex - cit - ing, _____

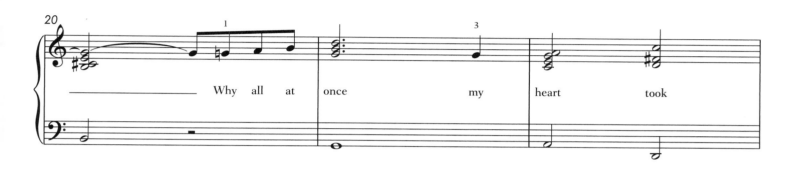

_____ Why all at once my heart took

flight. _____ I on - ly know when he _____ be - gan to

dance with me, _____ I could have danced, danced,

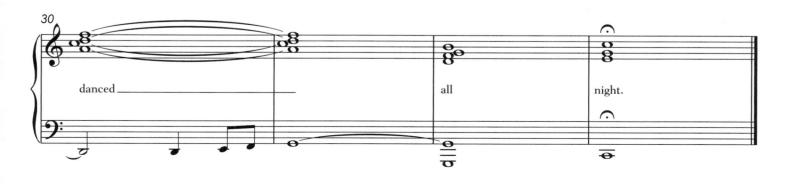

danced _____ all night.

DON'T RAIN ON MY PARADE
(FROM *FUNNY GIRL*)

Words by Bob Merrill
Music by Jule Styne

band out, __ I'll beat my drum. _____ And if I'm

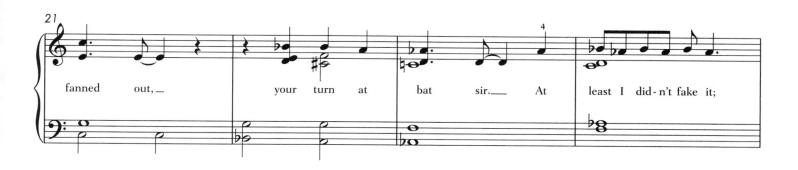

fanned out, __ your turn at bat sir. __ At least I did-n't fake it;

Hat, sir. __ I guess I did-n't make it! Get rea-dy for me __

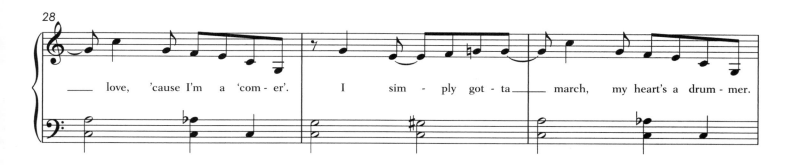

__ love, 'cause I'm a 'com-er'. I sim-ply got-ta __ march, my heart's a drum-mer.

Don't bring __ a-round a __ cloud to rain on my pa- rade. _____

I GOT RHYTHM
(FROM *GIRL CRAZY*)

Music and Lyrics by George Gershwin and Ira Gershwin

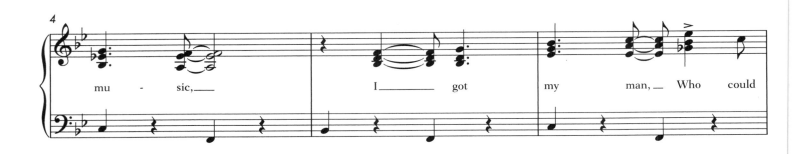

AND ALL THAT JAZZ
(FROM *CHICAGO*)

Words by Fred Ebb
Music by John Kander

CONSIDER YOURSELF
(FROM OLIVER!)

Words and Music by Lionel Bart

LUCK BE A LADY
(FROM *GUYS AND DOLLS*)

Words and Music by Frank Loesser

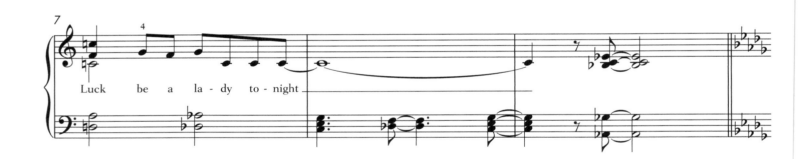

Luck be a la-dy with me.

la - dy does - n't leave her es - cort It is - n't fair, it is - n't

nice. A la - dy does - n't wan - der all o - ver the room and

blow on some o - ther guy's dice. So let's keep the par - ty po - lite

Ne - ver get out of my sight. Stick with me ba - by, I'm the

fel - low you came in with, Luck be a la - dy to - night.

ANYTHING GOES
(FROM *ANYTHING GOES*)

Words and Music by Cole Porter

Upbeat, swung ♩ = c.176

In old - en days a glimpse of stock - ing Was looked on as some - thing shock -

- ing, But now God knows,＿＿＿ An - y - thing goes. Good

au - thors, too, who once knew bet - ter words Now on - ly use four - let - ter words, writ - ing

prose,＿＿＿ An - y - thing goes. The world＿ has gone

mad to-day— And good's bad to-day,— And black's white to-day,— And day's night to-day,—When most

guys to-day— That wom-en prize to-day— Are just sil-ly gi-go-los.— So

though I'm not a great ro-man-cer I know that you're bound to an-swer when I pro-

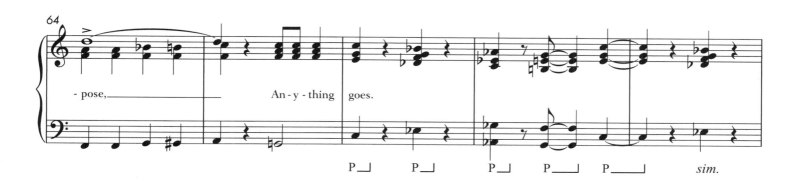

-pose,_____ An-y-thing goes.

FLASHDANCE (WHAT A FEELING)
(FROM *FLASHDANCE*)

Words by Irene Cara and Keith Forsey
Music by Giorgio Moroder

FAME
(FROM *FAME*)

Words by Dean Pitchford
Music by Michael Gore

45

SEND IN THE CLOWNS
(FROM *A LITTLE NIGHT MUSIC*)

Words and Music by Stephen Sondheim

knowing the one that I wanted was yours, Making my

entrance again with my usual flair, Sure of my

lines, No-one is there. Don't you love

farce? My fault, I fear. I thought that you'd want what I want; sorry, my

dear. But where are the clowns? Quick, send in the

clowns. Don't bother, they're here.

SUMMER NIGHTS
(FROM GREASE)

Words and Music by Jim Jacobs and Warren Casey

Tell me more, tell me more, but you don't got to brag.___ Tell me more, tell me

more, 'cos he sounds like a drag.___

He got friend-ly,____ hold-ing my hand.____ She got friend-ly,____

down in the sand.____ He was sweet, just turned eigh-teen.__

She was good. You know what I mean.__ Sum-mer heat,

boy and girl meet.__ But__ uh, oh those sum-mer nights.___

MAMMA MIA
(FROM *MAMMA MIA!*)

Words and Music by Benny Andersson, Björn Ulvaeus and Stig Anderson

1. I've been cheat-ed by you since I don't know when,
2. I've been an-gry and sad a-bout things that you do,

so I made up my mind it must come to an end,
I can't count all the times that I've told you we're through,

look at me now, will I ev-er learn? I don't know how,
and when you go, when you slam the door, I think you know

but I sud-den-ly lose con-trol, there's a fire with-in my soul.
that you won't be a-way too long, you know that I'm not that strong.

Just one look and I can hear a bell ring,——— one more look and I for-get ev-'ry-thing,———

——— oh,— oh,— Mam-ma mi- a, here I go a-gain, my, my, how——

——— can I re-sist you? Mam-ma mi- a, does it show a-gain, my, my, just———

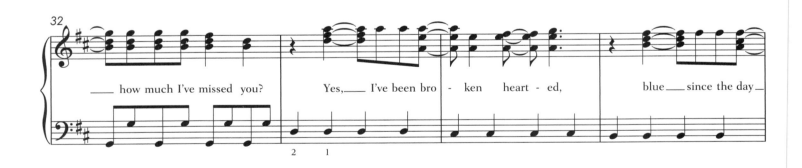

——— how much I've missed you? Yes,— I've been bro- ken heart- ed, blue——since the day——

3rd time to Coda

——— we part- ed, why, why did——— I ev-er let you go?——— Mam-ma mi- a,

now I real-ly know, my, my, I could ne-ver let you go. e-ven if I say

bye - bye, leave me now or ne - ver. Mam-ma mi-a, it's a game we play,

D.S. al Coda   Coda

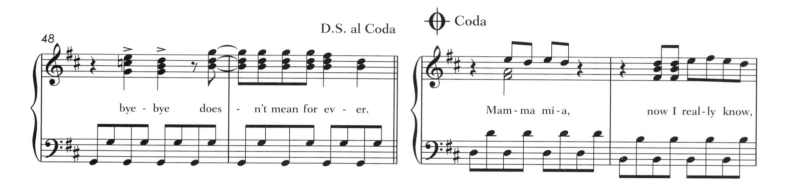

bye - bye does - n't mean for ev - er. Mam-ma mi-a, now I real-ly know,

my, my, I could ne-ver let you go.

MEMORY
(FROM CATS)

Music by Andrew Lloyd Webber
Text by Trevor Nunn after T.S. Eliot

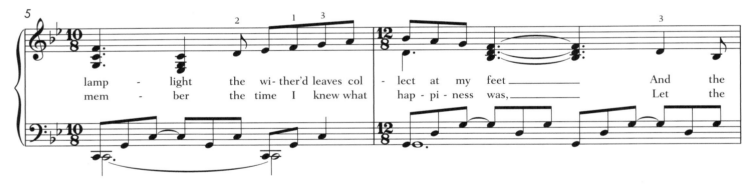

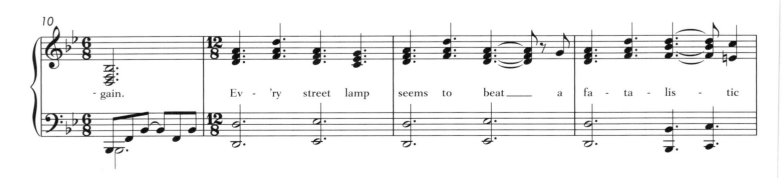

(I'VE HAD) THE TIME OF MY LIFE
(FROM *DIRTY DANCING*)

Words and Music by Frankie Previte,
John De Nicola and Donald Markowitz

writ-ing on the wall,____ as we felt this ma-gi-cal fan-ta - sy.____ *Both:* Now with

pas-sion in our eyes____ there's no way we could dis-guise_ it se-cret-ly____

So we take each o-ther's hand____ 'cos we seem to un-der-stand the ur-gen-

- cy.____ *(Boy, spoken:)* 'Just remember' *Girl:* You're the one thing *Boy:* I can't get e-nough

of *Girl:* So I'll tell you some-thing *Both:* This could be love be - cause

I've had the time of my life, no I've ne-ver felt this way be-

-fore, yes I swear it's the truth, and I owe it all to you.

Girl: With my bo-dy and soul I want you

more than you'll e-ver know. *Boy:* So we'll

just let it go don't be a-fraid to lose con-trol *Girl:* Yes I

know what's on your mind___ when you say_ 'stay with me to - night' _____

(Boy, spoken:) 'Just remember'   *Boy:* You're the one thing   *Girl:* I can't get e - nough of

Boy: So I'll tell you some - thing   *Both:* This could be love be - cause

f I've ___ had the time of my life,_____ no I've ne - ver felt this way be-
I've ___ had the time of my life_____ and I've searched through ev - 'ry op - en

repeat and fade

- fore,_____ yes I swear_____ it's the truth, ___ and I owe it all to you, 'cos___
door,_____ 'til I found _____ the truth, ___ and I owe it all to you._____

For more in a chilled mood try the rest of the series ... each with a free Naxos CD

Adagio Chillout
Favourite slow movements and contemplative pieces, including Beethoven's *Moonlight Sonata*, Schumann's *Träumerei* and Mendelssohn's *Song without words 'Sweet Remembrance'*.

0-571-52435-4

Chill with Chopin
Including masterpieces such as the *'Raindrop'* Prelude, the *March Funèbre* from Sonata in B flat minor, and the Waltz in A flat *'L'Adieu'*.

0-571-52438-9

Chill with Mozart
The most beautiful movements by Mozart, including the first movement from Sonata in C K.545, the Fantasia in D minor K.397 and Adagio in B minor K.540.

0-571-52436-2

Chill with Debussy
Unmissable favourites such as *Clair de lune*, *La fille aux cheveux de lin* and *Arabesque* No.1.

0-571-52437-0

To buy Faber Music publications or to find out about the full range of titles available please contact your local music retailer or Faber Music sales enquiries:

Faber Music Ltd, Burnt Mill, Elizabeth Way, Harlow CM20 2HX
Tel: +44 (0) 1279 82 89 82   Fax: +44 (0) 1279 82 89 83
sales@fabermusic.com   fabermusic.com   expressprintmusic.com